Nikolai Kapustin
Николай Капустин
1937 – 2020

Gingerbread Man

(2003)

for Piano
für Klavier
для фортепиано

opus 111

Authorized Version

ED 23033
ISMN 979-0-001-20499-6

www.schott-music.com

Mainz · London · Madrid · Paris · New York · Tokyo · Beijing
© 2021 Schott Music GmbH & Co. KG, Mainz · Printed in Germany

Gingerbread Man

opus 111

Nikolai Kapustin
1937–2020

Con brio (♩ = 184)

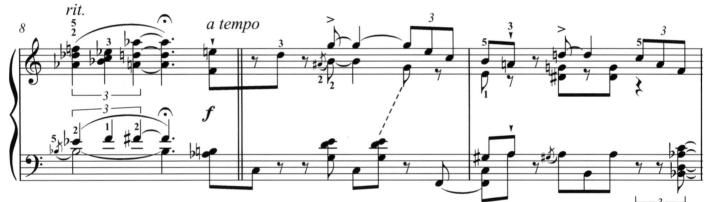

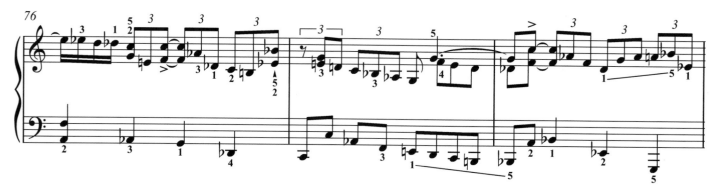

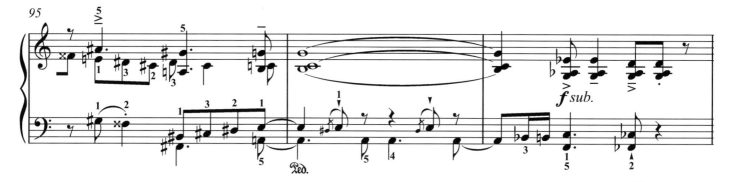

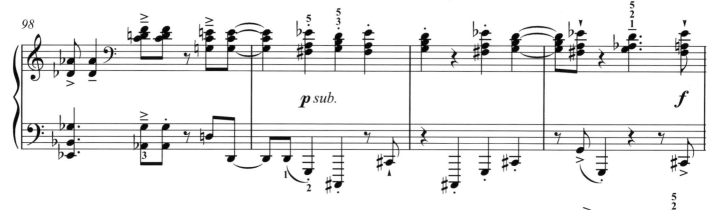

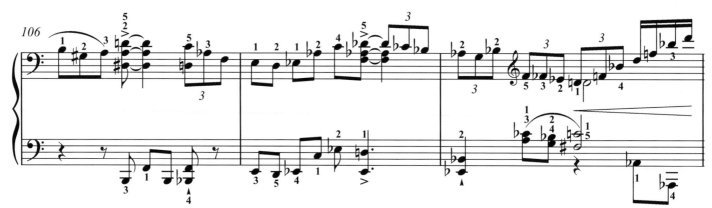

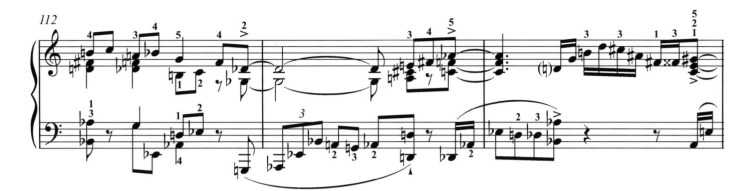

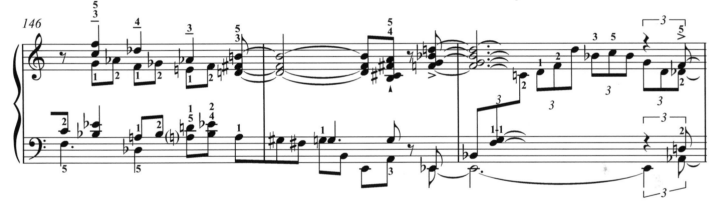

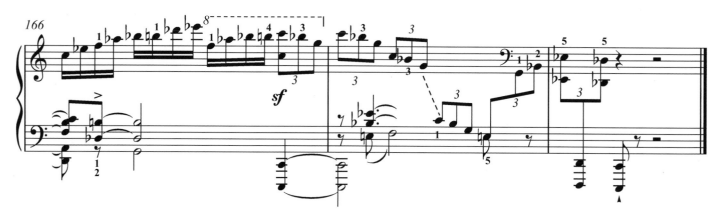

Schott Music, Mainz 59 371